# GREAT EXPECTATIONS

by
Charles Dickens

## Student Packet

Written by
Gloria Levine, M.A.

**Contains masters for:**

| | |
|---|---|
| 1 | Prereading Activity |
| 1 | Study Guide (seven pages) |
| 10 | Vocabulary Activities |
| 3 | Characterization Activities |
| 3 | Literary Analysis/Critical Thinking Activities |
| 1 | Review Activity |
| 1 | Writing Response Activity |
| 11 | Essay Topics |
| 2 | Comprehension Quizzes (two levels) |
| 2 | Unit Exams (two levels) |
| **PLUS** | Detailed Answer Key |

**Note**

The text used to prepare this guide was the Penguin Classics softcover published by The Penguin Group, edited by Angus Calder. Introduction and notes ©1965 by Penguin Books Ltd. The page references may differ in other editions.

**Please note:** Please assess the appropriateness of this book for the age level and maturity of your students prior to reading and discussing it with your class.

**ISBN 1-56137-515-2**



Printed in the United States of America.

**To order, contact your local school supply store, or—**

**Novel Units, Inc.**
**P.O. Box 97**
**Bulverde, TX 78163-0097**

**Web site: www.educyberstor.com**

Name____________________________

*Great Expectations*
Activity #1: **Journal Topics**
Use Before and During Reading

**I.** Dickens often gave his characters names that fit their personalities. Before you read the novel, describe how you imagine each of the following characters, based on their names alone:

1. Pip
2. Miss Havisham
3. Mr. Wopsle
4. Mr. Pumblechook
5. Mr. Jaggers
6. Orlick
7. Estella
8. Miss Skiffins
9. Bentley Drummle
10. Abel Magwitch

**II.** Use the following sentence-starters for freewriting in your literature response journal. Choose one topic before you begin reading. Then select others as you read. Spend about five minutes on each entry.

1. Getting jilted at the altar...
2. A child can be frightened into keeping a secret...
3. A child will lie if...
4. To feel ashamed of your home or family...
5. Being infatuated with someone...
6. Children who are beaten...
7. If you accept money that is ill-gotten...
8. Forgiveness...
9. When children are raised by people other than their parents...
10. Being a member of a wealthy group of society...

Name____________________________

*Great Expectations*
**Study Questions**
Use During Reading

**Directions:** Write a brief answer to each study question as you read the novel at home or in class. Use the questions for review before group discussions and before your novel test.

* = prediction, no right or wrong answer
** = thought question, no right or wrong answer

**Chapters 1-7**

1. Where does Pip meet the convict? What is Pip doing there?
2. What does the convict order Pip to do? Why does Pip obey?
3. What is Tickler? What does Pip mean, "I often served as a connubial missile"? (page 41)
4. What is Tar-water? How does it get into the brandy Mr. Pumblechook drinks?
5. When Pip takes the food to the convict, whom does he first meet on the marsh? How does the convict act when Pip mentions that encounter?
6. Whom does Pip's sister invite for Christmas dinner? How do these guests treat Pip?
7. Why does Joe keep offering Pip more gravy?
8. Why do the soldiers want to see Joe?
9. Why is one of the convicts yelling "Murder" when the searchers discover him?
10. What does the convict lie about and why?
11. Explain what Pip means when he says, "I was too cowardly to do what I knew to be right, as I had been too cowardly to avoid doing what I knew to be wrong." (page 72)
12. How does Pip learn to read and write?
13. Why does Mr. Pumblechook take Pip to town?

* **PREDICTION:** What will Miss Havisham be like? How will Pip "play" at Miss Havisham's?

** What do you "see" in your imagination when Pip brings the convict food and a file?

**Chapters 8-12**

1. Pip says "I discovered a singular affinity between seeds and corduroys." (page 83) What is another way of saying the same thing?
2. How does Mr. Pumblechook's breakfast contrast with the one he gives Pip?
3. How does the girl who lets Pip in at the gate of Miss Havisham's treat Pip?
4. When Pip sees Miss Havisham, why does he think of the waxwork he had been taken to see at the Fair?
5. How do Pip and Estella entertain Miss Havisham?
6. Why does Pip cry?
7. What does Pip imagine he sees in the garden? (page 94)

8. Why doesn't Pip describe to his sister what he saw at Miss Havisham's?
9. Explain what Pip means when he says, "Whitewash on the forehead hardens the brain into a state of obstinacy perhaps." (page 95)
10. How does Pip know that the stranger at the Jolly Bargeman knows the convict? What does the stranger give Pip?
11. Whom does Pip meet at Miss Havisham's, the second time he visits? How does Miss Havisham seem to get along with these people?
12. When does Estella let Pip kiss her? Why doesn't he enjoy the victory over the "pale gentleman"—or the kiss?
13. Whom does Pip trust enough to tell everything—even the story of the fight with the pale gentleman?
14. Whom does Miss Havisham tell Pip to bring along on his next visit? Why does Pip's sister "go on the rampage" about this?

* **PREDICTION:** The adult narrator says that he "could have had no foresight then, that [the burly man he met at Miss Havisham's] ever would be anything to me." (page 111) How do you think their paths cross in the future? The adult narrator also says that he now knows "the pain [Estella] cost me afterwards." How do you think she hurts him later?

** Dickens is often simultaneously serious and comic (seriocomic or ironic). On a scale of 1 to 7, how comic do you think he is being at the beginning of this section (Chapter 8)? What about at the end of the section (Chapter 12)? Why do you think so?

**Chapters 13-18**

1. What does Miss Havisham want from Joe? How can you tell that he is nervous?
2. What does Miss Havisham give Pip? Why? Why does she call Joe back?
3. Pip says that he has "reason to think that Joe's intellects were brightened by the encounter [with Miss Havisham] because of what took place afterward in Mr. Pumblechook's parlor. (page 130) Explain what happened.
4. What does it mean to be "bound"? Who takes Pip to be bound?
5. How do Pip's feelings about his home change? Why?
6. "It was not because I was faithful, but because Joe was faithful, that I never ran away and went for a soldier or a sailor." (page135) Explain what this means.
7. To whom does Pip turn for help in learning all that he can? Why does he decline further instruction from Mr. Wopsle?
8. When Pip talks to Joe about visiting Miss Havisham, Joe starts talking about door-chains, toasting-forks, gridirons, etc. (page 139) Why?
9. Who is Orlick and why does Pip compare him to Cain? (page140)

10. Why do Orlick and Joe have a fistfight?
11. Estella is away when Pip visits Miss Havisham. Where is Estella?
12. How does Pip's sister get injured? Whom does Pip suspect?
13. "Mr. Wopsle's great-aunt conquered a confirmed habit of living into which she had fallen." What does this mean? How does this affect Biddy?
14. How does Pip's sister change in her attitude toward Orlick after the attack?
15. What news does Jaggers bring Pip?

* **PREDICTION:** Pip speculates about what "might have been" between Biddy and him if he hadn't met Estella. Do you think he will ever get together with Biddy? What will happen to Pip's sister? How will his training as a gentleman go?

** Do any of the characters in this section remind you of people you have known? For example, have you ever known a Mr. Wopsle or a Mr. Jaggers or a Biddy? How was the real person like the character?

<u>Chapters 19-23</u>

1. What does Pip argue with Biddy about, before he leaves? (page 176)
2. Mr. Trabb greets Pip in a "hail-fellow-well-met" kind of way. How has his attitude toward Pip changed? Why?
3. How does Trabb's boy feel about Pip?
4. Before going to London, Pip says good-bye to Miss Havisham. Why does he refer to her as his "fairy godmother"? (page184)
5. How can you tell that Jaggers seems to care more about money than about helping his clients?
6. Who is Herbert Pocket? How does Pip know him from before?
7. What does Herbert decide to call Pip?
8. What does Pip learn from Herbert about Miss Havisham's past?
9. What is Herbert's mother's chief complaint?
10. How many children are in Herbert's family? Would you say that this is a "big, happy family"?

* **PREDICTION:** How will Pip get along with Herbert? with his tutor, Herbert's father? with Drummle and Startop, the other two boarders?

** Have you ever experienced any of the incidents described in this section? For example, have you ever avoided being seen with a parent or guardian you love, for fear of embarrassment—as Pip avoids being seen with Joe? Have you ever asked someone to help you "improve yourself"—as Pip asks Herbert? How was your experience like the one in the book?

## Chapters 24-30

1. Why does Pip ask Mr. Jaggers for 20 pounds? Does he get it?
2. Wemmick paid Pip his money after he had "put all the biscuit into the post." (page 222) What does that mean?
3. Where did Wemmick get his brooch? What does he mean, "My guiding star always is—get hold of portable property"?
4. Who is the sulky, idle, rich, suspicious student of Mr. Pocket's?
5. Who are Camilla and Georgiana? Why do they hate Pip?
6. Why does Jaggers leave his doors unlocked, according to Wemmick?
7. How is Wemmick's house different from the office where he works?
8. Who is "the Aged"? How does Wemmick treat him?
9. Whom does Jaggers invite to dinner? In which guest is Jaggers particularly interested?
10. What is unusual about Jaggers' housekeeper?
11. Why does Pip return after dinner to apologize to Jaggers?
12. Why does Biddy write to Pip? Why do you think she doesn't read the last line of her letter to Joe? (page 240)
13. Why does Pip return to his home town the day after Joe's visit?
14. Who is the Avenger?
15. The convicts sit behind Pip in the coach. Where has Pip seen one of them before?
16. Why does the waiter at the Blue Boar put the old newspaper near Pip?
17. How has Estella changed? How has she remained the same?
18. Why does Pip think that Estella is destined for him? What does Miss Havisham tell him repeatedly to do? (page 261)
19. How and why does Pip cause Orlick to be fired?
20. How does Trabb's boy treat Pip? How was Trabb's boy treated when Pip was outfitted for his first trip to London?

* **PREDICTION:** When—if ever—will Estella begin to be interested in Pip? Will they get together?

** If you were making a movie based on the book, whom would you cast as Drummle? Whom would you cast as Orlick? How do you imagine each of these to look? How are these two alike? How are they different? If you were to "flesh out" these minor characters, what details might you add to their description in the story?

## Chapters 31-37

1. What play do Herbert and Pip go to see? How can you tell which play it is? Is the acting good?
2. Why does Wemmick visit Newgate?

3. How does Pip learn that Estella is on her way to London? Why is she going there?
4. "We spent as much money as we could, and got as little for it as people could make up their minds to give us." (page 293) What tone of voice do you imagine Pip using here? What is he saying? How is the money being spent?
5. Why does Biddy have to leave her position in Pip's boyhood home? What kind of job will she get?
6. What does Mr. Jaggers give Pip on his 21st birthday?
7. Who is Miss Skiffins?
8. When Pip asks Wemmick's opinion about lending money, Wemmick responds that his opinion would be different in different places. What does he mean?
9. How does Pip help Herbert—without Herbert's knowledge?
10. How does Miss Skiffins seem to feel about Wemmick's advances?

* **PREDICTION:** Pip feels a "nameless shadow" pass when he sees Estella's face at the window of the coach. What do you think that fleeting thought or memory might be?

** How does Newgate compare with an American prison today? Do you get the sense that Pip feels sorry for the prisoners there? What about Jaggers and Wemmick? How do you think Dickens feels about the prison?

<u>Chapters 38-43</u>

1. How does Estella "torture" Pip while she stays with Mrs. Brandley?
2. Why does Miss Havisham call Estella an "ingrate"? (page 322)
3. How does Pip first learn that Drummle has his eye on Estella?
4. How does Pip learn who his benefactor really is? Who else knows?
5. Where has Pip's benefactor been all this time?
6. Why must Pip keep the convict's whereabouts a secret?
7. What is the convict's real name? What name does he go by now?
8. Who helps Pip come up with a plan for getting the convict out of the country?
9. Who is Compeyson? What is his connection with the convict? What is his connection with Miss Havisham?
10. How does Pip learn that Estella is having dinner with Drummle?

* **PREDICTION:** What do you think Drummle means by snidely asking Pip if he hasn't lost enough already? (page 371) What do you think will happen to the convict?

** Pip sees Miss Havisham and Estella argue in this section. Could Estella have been a more warm and caring person, if she had wanted to be—despite Miss Havisham's influence?

**Chapters 44-50**

1. What does Miss Havisham say when Pip accuses her of leading him on to think that she was his benefactor?
2. Who is Estella going to marry? Why?
3. Who writes to Pip "Don't Go Home"? Why not?
4. Wemmick finds a place for "Tom, Jack, or Richard" to stay. Who is "Tom, Jack, or Richard"? Where will he stay?
5. Who is Clara? How can you tell that she is kind and selfless?
6. Why does Mr. Wopsle glare so strangely at Pip during the performance?
7. What idiosyncratic personal habit does Mr. Jaggers have?
8. Why does Pip think that Molly is Estella's mother?
9. What does Wemmick know about Molly's past?
10. How does Miss Havisham help Herbert?
11. What does Miss Havisham reveal about how she acquired Estella? What does Miss Havisham ask Pip to sign?
12. Why does Pip return to Miss Havisham's room shortly after he leaves? What does he find there?
13. How does Pip find out that Provis's wife, like Estella's mother, was a murderess with a young daughter?

* **PREDICTION:** Will Pip tell Estella—or the convict—what he knows about their relationship?

** Do any of the incidents or themes in this section remind you of articles you find in newspapers? Have you read about real people who have evaded the law for many years—and then been recaptured? How was their situation like or different from Provis's? Have you read about any real-life criminals whose stories remind you of Jaggers' housekeeper's life? Have you ever read about someone who suffers from a mental disorder like Miss Havisham's?

**Chapters 51-56**

1. Who is Estella's father? Whom does Pip tell? Why?
2. How did Estella end up being raised by Miss Havisham?
3. How does Jaggers argue against telling the secret of Estella's parentage? Does Pip agree? Do you agree?
4. Why do Jaggers and Wemmick order Mike out of the office?
5. Where is Herbert's job going to take him? Why isn't Pip surprised when Herbert announces that he will be going to "the land of the Arabian nights"? (page 428)
6. Who is Startop and what does Herbert ask him to do?
7. Why does Pip go alone to the sluice-house? What danger does he find there?

8. How does Herbert save Pip's life?
9. Why don't Herbert and Pip pursue Orlick?
10. How is the convict caught?
11. How did Compeyson know where to find the convict?
12. What happens to Compeyson?
13. Why does Wemmick take Pip to church?
14. What happens at the convict's trial?
15. What does Pip tell the convict right before the convict dies?

* **PREDICTION:** What will happen to Pip now? Will he see Estella again?

** Were there any parts of this section that made you smile? that shocked you? that surprised you? Did you find the scene where the convict dies moving or too melodramatic? Were you surprised that Pip told him about Estella?

**Chapters 57-59 and Appendices**

1. What happens to Pip after the convict dies?
2. How does Pip learn about Miss Havisham's will? What does he learn?
3. What happens to Orlick?
4. Pip is in trouble with his debtors before he grows ill. Why isn't he being pursued by them after he recovers?
5. What does Pip plan to say to Biddy? Why doesn't he say it?
6. How does Pip spend the next 11 years after Joe's wedding?
7. What has Pip heard about Estella's married life?
8. When and where does Pip see Estella again at the end?
9. How has Estella changed? Will she part again from Pip?

* **PREDICTION:** Do you think Pip and Estella will be happy together?

** How do you think Pip feels when he learns that Miss Havisham is dead? that Orlick is in jail? that Joe and Biddy have just been married? when he sees Joe and Biddy's children? when he first sees Estella at Satis, after 11 years have passed?

Name______________________________



**Directions:** Choose the given word's synonym from among the four choices.

1. ___ trenchant (page 42)
(a) forceful (b) arid (c) attentive (d) impregnable
2. ___ remonstrance (page 43)
(a) exaggeration (b) protest (c) warning (d) threat
3. ___ augmented (page 45)
(a) enlarged (b) tallied (c) divided (d) eluded
4. ___ imprecations (page 52)
(a) debates (b) rumors (c) falsehoods (d) expletives
5. ___ dissuading (page 54)
(a) bolting (b) imbruing (c) coaxing (d) deterring
6. ___ contumaciously (page 59)
(a) obstinately (b) reproachfully (c) patiently (d) obediently
7. ___ imperious (page 60)
(a) explicit (b) disconsolate (c) constitutional (d) autocratic
8. ___ execrating (page 67)
(a) conversing (b) flouncing (c) cursing (d) foreshadowing
9. ___ pilfering (page 71)
(a) losing (b) stealing (c) overthrowing (d) retaining
10. ___ exonerated (page 71)
(a) located (b) exculpated (c) defeated (d) seized
11. ___ venerated (page 74)
(a) decanted (b) dispatched (c) isolated (d) respected
12. ___ erudition (page 75)
(a) learnedness (b) gibbet (c) larceny (d) deliverance
13. ___ perspicuity (page 77)
(a) bewilderment (b) lucidity (c) consternation (d) verification
14. ___ sagaciously (page 78)
(a) unceremoniously (b) wisely (c) prodigiously (d) blithely
15. ___ ablution (page 83)
(a) vestry (b) declamation (c) salutation (d) cleansing

Name______________________________

*Great Expectations*
Activity #3: **Vocabulary**
Chapters 8-12

**Directions:** Write a brief definition for each word, then place the words (by number) in the sentences that follow.

1. gourmandising (page 84) ____________________________________________
2. transfixed (page 91) ____________________________________________
3. capricious (page 92) ____________________________________________
4. ignominiously (page 95) ____________________________________________
5. adamantine (page 95) ____________________________________________
6. felicitous (page 101) ____________________________________________
7. appalled (page 120) ____________________________________________
8. sanguinary (page 121) ____________________________________________
9. trepidation (page 121) ____________________________________________
10. unremunerative (page 125) ____________________________________________

A. The disgraced leader is being treated ________ by the press.

B. She was ___________ with awe and could not take her eyes from the scene.

C. I can't believe that he would make a joke out of this; I am_________ by his insensitivity.

D. That battle was a particularly ___________ struggle.

E. He is a glutton who eats in a _______________ way; someone should give him a lesson in table manners.

F. He found that delivering pizza was rather ___________ work and decided to try for a more profitable job.

G. The shy five-year-old stood at the door to her new classroom and looked around with ___________.

H. The speaker opened her talk with a _________ remark that set everyone at ease.

I. She was rather _____________ as a child, but now she is much less erratic.

J. Don't try to change his mind; his opinions are ______________.

**Directions:** The SAT and PSAT include 19 analogies and 19 sentence completions. This exercise will give you practice with sentence completions.

| | | | | |
|---|---|---|---|---|
| arraying 127 | augur 127 | epitaph 128 | impostor 131 | diabolical 131 |
| benevolent 131 | beneficent 133 | vagaries 133 | retributive 134 | gridiron 139 |
| journeyman 139 | affront 140 | maudlin 145 | benefactor 145 | lee 145 |
| surmising 146 | corroborated 148 | contention 149 | aberration 150 | propitiation 151 |
| spectre 152 | disengaged 168 | pugilistic 168 | placable 169 | expostulatory 169 |
| valedictory 169 | rustic 171 | | | |

1. He learned his ________ skills from his father, a professional boxer.
   (A) pugilistic (B) benevolent (C) retributive
   (D) sanctified (E) industrious

2. She corresponded for years with the anonymous ________ who had paid for her education.
   (A) sluice-keeper (B) Fury (C) vagary
   (D) lee (E) benefactor

3. Her first story was a _______ tale about an orphan and her lost kitten.
   (A) mollified (B) maudlin (C) malevolent
   (D) latent (E) expostulatory

4. The villagers put gifts at the base of the volcano for the ____________ of the wrathful gods.
   (A) propitiation (B) valedictory (C) spectre
   (D) contention (E) aberration

5. His sister holds a grudge, but luckily he is a(n) _______ child.
   (A) inscrutable (B) unscrupulous (C) placable
   (D) morose (E) pugilistic

6. Her habitual house cleaning was a kind of ______________.
   (A) industry (B) gridiron (C) hazard
   (D) disparagement (E) aberration

7. He is usually honest, but will resort to __________ if he thinks it's necessary to get what he wants.
   (A) preliminary (B) rustic (C) indentured
   (D) diabolical (E) arraying

8. He refused to wear the party hat as he considered it a(n) ________ to his dignity.
   (A) valedictory (B) affront (C) assailant
   (D) contention (E) aberration

9. I do not know for certain how old she is, but I am __________ that she must be at least 40.
   (A) surmising (B) patronizing (C) alienating
   (D) disengaging (E) propitiating

10. He said he was ill on Saturday and his sister ________ his excuse.
   (A) ill-requited (B) corroborated (C) unwonted
   (D) obtruded (E) reciprocated

Name______________________________



**Directions:** This exercise will give you practice in one of the question types that appears in the verbal sections of the SAT: antonymns. Circle the word that means the opposite of the given word.

*Sample:* X. DUPLICITY: (A) vulnerability (B) division (C) utility (D) honesty (E) tranquility

**Answer:** D

1. OBSCURELY: (A) cunningly (B ) reasonably (C) correctly (D) ironically (E) conspicuously
2. AUDACIOUS: (A) cowardly (B) diligent (C) dishonest (D) faithful (E) unstable
3. AFFABLE: (A) shrewd (B) decisive (C) uncivil (D) inept (E) untrustworthy
4. UNWONTED: (A) accurate (B) usual (C) appealing (D) homely (E) formal
5. GUILELESS: (A) wily (B) meek (C) loyal (D) reckless (E) wasteful
6. DOLEFULLY: (A) wistfully (B) viciously (C) guiltily (D) soothingly (E) jubilantly
7. AVARICIOUS: (A) generous (B) patient (C) tactful (D) anxious (E) disgusted
8. COMPRESS: (A) vibrate (B) topple (C) expand (D) yank (E) accompany
9. UNRESERVEDLY: (A) silently (B) restrainedly (C) unscrupulously (D) honestly (E) steadily
10. INCIPIENT: (A) terminating (B) malevolent (C) concrete (D) initial (E) convenient
11. AMIABLE: (A) courteous (B) coarse (C) disagreeable (D) distracted (E) experienced
12. ABASHED: (A) unified (B) submissive (C) uninspired (D) unashamed (E) unassured
13. IRREPRESSIBLE: (A) compassionate (B) quarrelsome (C) inimical (D) manageable (E) consistent
14. ODIOUS: (A) offensive (B) delightful (C) creative (D) aromatic (E) chaotic
15. GENTEEL: (A) boorish (B) impressionable (C) urbane (D) malicious (E) infirm

Name_____________________________

*Great Expectations*
Activity #6: **Vocabulary**
Chapters 24-30

**Directions:** This exercise will give you practice with one of the question types that appear in the verbal sections of the PSAT and SAT: analogies. In each analogy question, you are given two words in capital letters that are related in a specific way. You must figure out how they are related, and then select from the answer choices a pair of words that are related in the same way.

***Sample:***
X. SUBMISSIVE: YIELD::
(A) aggressive: behave
(B) obedient: comply
(C) suspicious: believe
(D) pliable: rebuff
(E) permissive: pacify

1. **NIGGARDLY: HOARD**
(A) domineering: acquiesce
(B) attentive: ignore
(C) complacent: disapprove
(D) stodgy: beguile
(E) contemptuous: deride

2. **ADVERSARY: OPPONENT**
(A) publican: voter
(B) testator: spectator
(C) dolt: student
(D) patroness: benefactress
(E) purser: slave owner

3. **SPURIOUS: AUTHENTIC**
(A) diffident: unusual
(B) massive: puny
(C) felonious: dishonest
(D) amphibious: moist
(E) anomalous: incongruous

4. **RANKLED: RESENTMENT**
(A) peeved: anxiety
(B) frazzled: grief
(C) spurred: joy
(D) entertained: boredom
(E) grated: annoyance

5. **RETICENCE: CURB**
(A) ebullience: liberate
(B) curiosity: regain
(C) diligence: seize
(D) sincerity: inherit
(E) sluggishness: extract

6. **ABASED: DOWN**
(A) derogated: through
(B) mortified: out
(C) demeaned: alongside
(D) extolled: up
(E) acclaimed: down

7. **DESPONDENCY: FORLORN**
(A) hostility: jealous
(B) guilt: angry
(C) melancholy: woeful
(D) exasperation: sober
(E) jubilation: content

Name______________________________



**Directions:** Tell what the words in each pair have in common.

1. elocution (276)—lecture
2. approbation (277)—gratitude
3. fetters (280)—handcuffs
4. cistern (281)—well
5. subordinate (283)—private
6. turnkeys (283)—judges
7. suppliants (284)—panhandlers
8. pattens (285)—socks
9. ostler (288)—jockey
10. farthingale (290)—miniskirt
11. interment (297)—obituary
12. quarries (302)—coal mines
13. pilgrimage (311)—vacation
14. Union Jack (311)—stars and stripes
15. cestus (316)—sash

Name______________________________



**Directions:** For each word below, use context clues to write your own definition (what you think the word might mean). Then use a dictionary to check your definition. Write your revised definition in the third column.

| **Word/Page** | **Prediction of Definition Based on Context** | **Revised Definition** |
|---|---|---|
| 1. wan (321) | ______________ | ______________ |
| 2. sconces (321) | ______________ | ______________ |
| 3. ingrate 322 | ______________ | ______________ |
| 4. beseeching (326) | ______________ | ______________ |
| 5. untenable (327) | ______________ | ______________ |
| 6. dram (343) | ______________ | ______________ |
| 7. prolix (344) | ______________ | ______________ |
| 8. dubiously (345) | ______________ | ______________ |
| 9. uncouth (346) | ______________ | ______________ |
| 10. physiognomy (349) | ______________ | ______________ |
| 11. expatriated (351) | ______________ | ______________ |
| 12. pannikins (352) | ______________ | ______________ |
| 13. pretext (358) | ______________ | ______________ |
| 14. transport (359) | ______________ | ______________ |
| 15. vagrancy (362) | ______________ | ______________ |
| 16. extenuated (367) | ______________ | ______________ |
| 17. insolent (370) | ______________ | ______________ |
| 18. superciliously (371) | ______________ | ______________ |

Name________________________________



**Directions:** Write a brief definition next to each word. Then use the words to fill in the blanks in the sentences at the bottom.

1. plaited (380)
2. superannuated (387)
3. truculent (389)
4. necromantic (397)
5. tremulous (408)
6. blighted (409)
7. absolve (410)
8. entreated (410)
9. commiseration (412)
10. presentiment (413)
11. vestige (415)

12. Seeking forgiveness, Miss Havisham stretched out her ______ hand to Pip.
13. Miss Havisham wrote a note to __________ Pip of any suspicion that he would profit from the money intended for Herbert.
14. Clara's father growled like a _______ ogre.
15. When Miss Havisham got down on her knees, Pip was horrified and ________ her to rise.
16. The mother _______ her daughter's long hair.
17. Pip knew about Miss Havisham's past, and was filled with _______________ for her.
18. The fire burned every _________ of Miss Havisham's dress; not a scrap remained.

Name______________________________



**Directions:** Write the letter of the correct definition next to each word.

| |  | |  |
|---|---|---|---|
| _____ 1. | retrospectively (424) | a. | type of furnace |
| _____ 2. | obdurate (423) | b. | ominous |
| _____ 3. | limekiln (432) | c. | modest |
| _____ 4. | malignity (435) | d. | complaining |
| _____ 5. | gainsaying (442) | e. | introductory part of an oration |
| _____ 6. | tithe (445) | f. | board game with balls and cue |
| _____ 7. | hawsers (445) | g. | merciless |
| _____ 8. | vacillating (452) | h. | commanded earnestly |
| _____ 9. | adjured (454) | i. | contemplative of the past |
| _____10. | querulous (458) | j. | heavy ropes for mooring |
| _____11. | portentous (460) | k. | denounced; outlawed |
| _____12. | exordium (460) | l. | petitions; pleas |
| _____13. | discreet (463) | m. | blight; evil |
| _____14. | bagatelle (464) | n. | denying |
| _____15. | scourge (467) | o. | inspect; survey the enemy |
| _____16. | proscribed (467) | p. | wrong-doers; criminals |
| _____17. | appeals (468) | q. | a tenth, or indefinitely small part |
| _____18. | malefactors (468) | r. | faltering |
| _____19. | reconnoitre (453) | s. | draped gracefully with fabric |
| _____20. | festooned (447) | t. | sinister quality |

Name______________________________

*Great Expectations*
Activity #11: **Vocabulary**
Chapters 57-59

| | | |
|---|---|---|
| interminable 471 | transformations 472 | orthographical 474 |
| remonstrance 474 | codicil 474 | evasively 477 |
| slacken 479 | perplexity 479 | vestige 480 |
| assiduity 482 | ostentatious 483 | debilitating 484 |
| beguiled 486 | irrevocable 487 | |

**Directions:** Form a group of three and figure out the mystery words together. Then divide the remaining words between yourselves and make three clues for each one.

| | | |
|---|---|---|
| This five-syllable word is an adjective. | A spelling bee tests this kind of skill. | Part of this word is from the Greek "graphos"—something drawn or written. |

| | | |
|---|---|---|
| making weak or feeble | An illness like pneumonia can have this effect on your body. | from the Latin word, "debilis"—meaning "weak" |

| | | |
|---|---|---|
| This four-syllable adjective has three t's. | Meaning "intended to attract notice," this word contains the word for the numeral "X." | Lady Bountiful is this, but an anonymous donor is not. |

| | | |
|---|---|---|
| a very slight trace or amount of something | from the Latin word for footprint: "vestigium" | This word's ending rhymes with the ending of a word meaning "butchery" that starts with the letter c. |

Name______________________________



**Directions:** On the "spokes" surrounding each character's name, write several adjectives that describe that character at the end of "the first stage of Pip's expectations." On the arrows joining one character to another, write a description of the relationship between the two characters. How does one character influence the other?

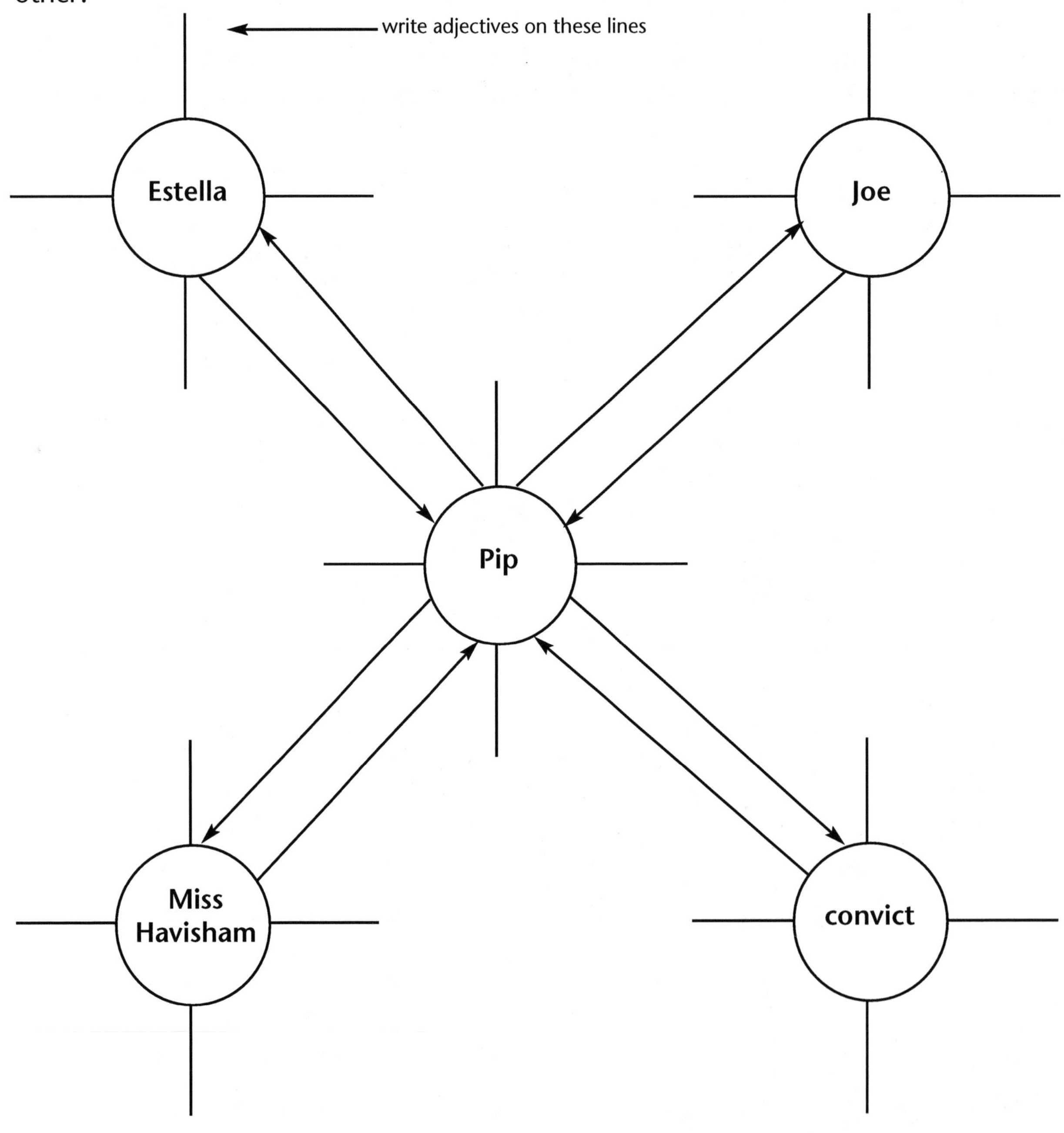

Name________________________________



**Directions:** Both Estella and Pip are raised by less-than-loving mother figures. Compare and contrast Miss Havisham and Mrs. Joe Gargery using the chart below. Write characteristics they share in the overlapping area, and unique characteristics in the outer areas.

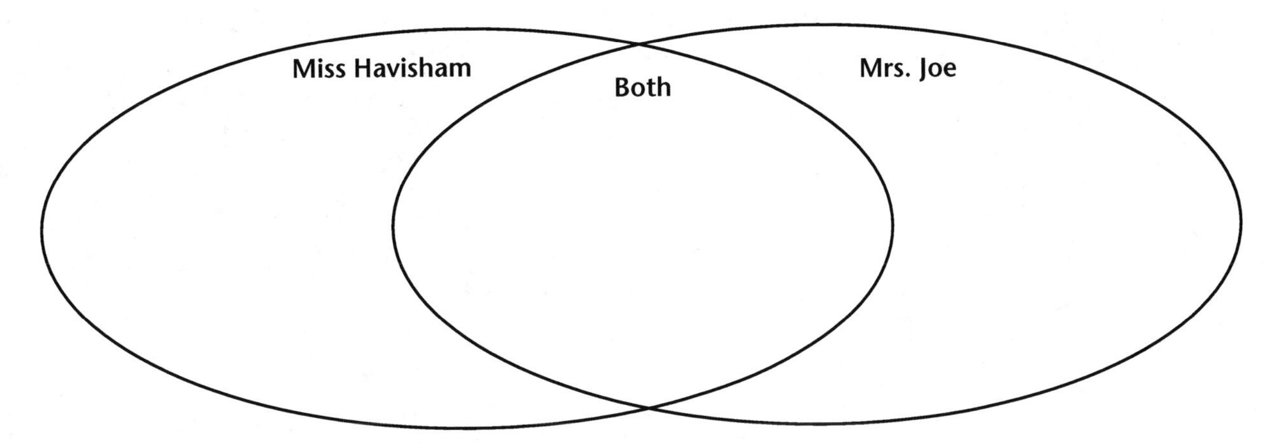


State your viewpoint on the following issue:

**Considering the emotionally unhealthy homes in which they were raised, can Estella and Pip be blamed for abusing those who loved them?**

Write five specific examples or details from the novel that support your viewpoint.

**Viewpoint:** ____ Yes ____ No

Detail #1:

Detail #2:

Detail #3:

Detail #4:

Detail #5:

Name______________________________



**Directions:** Below is a "spider map," an outline showing a central idea and the ideas that support it. Make an outline of ideas that support the following thesis:

**Coincidence plays a prominent role in *Great Expectations.***

Your completed outline should include at least four main ideas and at least eight details. Develop your outline into an essay on separate paper.

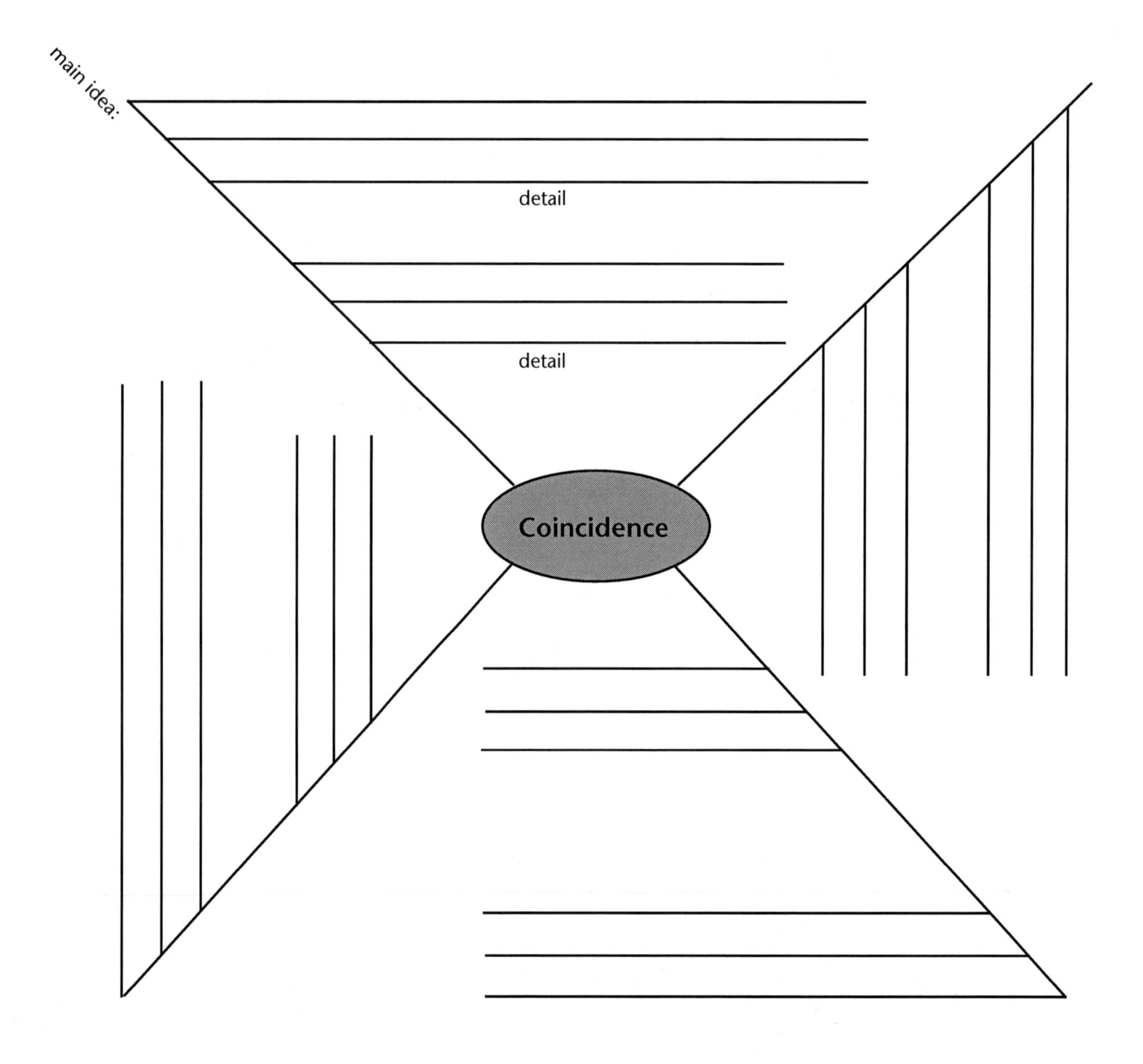

Name________________________________



**Directions:** Place each character below in one or more of the boxes. Discuss in a small group why you think the characters in a given box belong together.

Characters:

| | | | | |
|---|---|---|---|---|
| Pip | Miss Havisham | Estella | Joe Gargery | Mrs. Joe |
| Jaggers | Wemmick | Pumblechook | Herbert | Compeyson |
| Drummle | Magwitch | Orlick | | |

| VICTIMS | VILLAINS | CAPITALIST EXPLOITERS |
|---|---|---|
| | | |

| STATUS-SEEKERS | GOOD GUYS | GENTLEMEN/WOMEN |
|---|---|---|
| | | |

| DOERS | TALKERS | WORKING PEOPLE |
|---|---|---|
| | | |

Name_______________________________



**Directions:** Complete the following chart in a cooperative learning group; you may want to transfer the chart to a large piece of butcher paper. Simply jot ideas that come to mind as you discuss each topic.

| Pip | Miss Havisham | Estella | Magwitch |
|---|---|---|---|
| Settings | Problems | Parts that created vivid mental images | What the story is really about |
| Values highlighted | Coincidence | Function of minor characters | Good parts for Reader's Theatre |

Name________________________________

*Great Expectations*
Activity #17: **Character Relationships**
Use After Reading

**Directions:** There is a "love triangle" of sorts between Pip, Estella, and Bentley Drummle.

**Part I**
Look at the words and phrases inside the triangle. Put those that describe each character under his or her name. Some may be used more than once and others, not at all.



**Pip**

________________________
________________________
________________________
________________________
________________________
________

**Bentley Drummle**

________________________
________________________
________________________
________________________
________________________
________

**Estella**

________________________
________________________
________________________
________________________
________________________
________

**Part II**
Jot down answers to these questions:

- What attracts Pip to Estella?
- What attracts Bentley Drummle to Estella?
- Why isn't Estella in love with either man?
- Why does Estella choose Bentley Drummle?

**Part III**
Write an essay analyzing the love triangle between Pip, Estella, and Bentley Drummle. Explain what generalization Dickens may be making about the influence of background and parenting on the romantic relationships we form as adults.

This activity is adapted from one based on *The Great Gatsby,* and found in *Writing About Literature* by Elizabeth Kahn, Carolyn Walter and Larry Johannessen (NCTE; © 1984; page 50).

Name_______________________________

*Great Expectations*
Activity #18: **Critical Thinking**
Use With Film

**Directions:** Before watching a film of this Dickens classic, discuss how you would make the book into a movie. Some questions to discuss are:

- In casting for the major roles, what physical/emotional qualities would you look for?
- What sorts of costumes would you need?
- Where would you do the filming?
- What music would you use for your soundtrack? Where would you have music play?
- With what scene would you open the movie?
- With what scene would you end?

During and After Viewing: On the chart below, jot down changes, additions, and deletions made when the story was adapted for film. Note differences in how the book and movie let you know what characters are like and what events have transpired.

| **Movie** | **Novel** |
|---|---|
| | |

Follow-Up Activities: Write a review of the movie, design a poster for the film, or write and produce a TV commercial promoting the movie.

Name________________________________



**Directions:** Talk about the following topics with a partner or in small group. Brainstorm a list of ideas for each topic. Then: a) choose one topic, b) draft a composition about it, c) read your composition to a partner, and d) revise the composition, making sure that every detail tells about the topic.

**Ideas:**

1. Wemmick is almost like two different people: one person at work, another at home. Are you one person at school or at your job—and another at home? Describe your two different roles.

2. Pip was infatuated with Estella. The more coldly she treated him, the more obsessed with her he became. Tell about an infatuation you have experienced yourself—or read about in another story.

3. Miss Havisham seeks revenge against men through Estella, because of a bad experience that she had with one man when she was young. Have you ever known or heard about a person in real life who reminds you of Miss Havisham?

4. Pip is ashamed now to remember that he was once embarrassed by Joe and ashamed to be seen with him. Have you ever been embarrassed to be seen with a friend or relative? Did you reject that person? How did you feel about your actions later on?

Name________________________________



# Ideas for Essays

1. Write an essay in which you support or refute one of these statements, using evidence from the story: (a) In the end, Pip was what he wanted to be—a true gentleman. (b) In a class society, there is justice for the rich but none for the poor. (c) Class divisions sustained by wealth destroy the bonds of fellowship between men.
2. How does Dickens use movement in the novel, specifically movement between the marsh country where Pip lives as a boy, Miss Havisham's Satis House and London?
3. How does imprisonment play a part in this novel—not just the convict's imprisonment, but also Miss Havisham's and that of other characters whose daily lives seem to be prisons?
4. What coincidences occur in the novel? Does Dickens overdo coincidence in this story?
5. Find passages that show Dickens' use of sentimentality. For example, examine the scene where the convict dies with tears in his eyes. How do you feel about these instances of sentimentality?
6. Find passages where Dickens deliberately withholds information from his readers, but provides hints. Does this heighten interest in the story—or is it unfair and contrived?
7. Dickens loved theater. How is *Great Expectations* theatrical? To what moments does the novel build? Which scenes have "stagy" qualities?
8. Which of the characters are most well-rounded? Which are the flattest? Which seem most real to you? Why?
9. This has been called one of Dickens' "happiest" novels. Compare it to other novels by Dickens and explain why this one might be considered "happier." How does Dickens combine bitterness and laughter in *Great Expectations?*
10. What themes does Dickens develop in this novel? Which of these themes are treated in other novels by Dickens? What insights does *Great Expectations* offer about the court system? about the independently wealthy? about the poor?
11. Choose one of the following themes and write an essay showing how it is developed in the course of the novel: *guilt, class divisions, the selfish pursuit of wealth, snobbery, moral rebirth, self-awareness.*

Name________________________________

*Great Expectations*
**Comprehension Quiz • Level I**
Use After Chapters 1-23

**True-False:** Mark each statement T or F. On the back of your paper, rewrite false statements to make them true.

___ 1. Pip helped the escaped convict because the convict gave him a shilling and two one-pound notes.

___ 2. Pip was raised by his older sister, who mistreated him by beating him and criticizing him constantly.

___ 3. Joe was kind to Pip and tried to help Pip avoid beatings by Mrs. Joe.

___ 4. When Pip first met Miss Havisham, he was astonished to see that she wore an old wedding dress and kept an old wedding cake covered with cobwebs.

___ 5. Estella made quite a contrast with Biddy: Estella was plain and kind while Biddy was beautiful and cold.

___ 6. Pip's sister became an invalid after she was hit over the head by an attacker.

___ 7. Pip's expectations changed for the better when Mr. Jaggers brought the news that Miss Havisham would pay to make him a gentleman

___ 8. When Pip got to London, he discovered that his tutor's son was familiar to him because they had played together as boys at Miss Havisham's.

___ 9. Pip began to understand Miss Havisham's attitude toward men when Herbert told him that 25 years earlier she had been jilted by her fiance on her wedding day.

___ 10. Mrs. Pocket's snobbery was evident from the way she complained continually about the fact that she had not married someone of noble birth.

**Vocabulary:** Write the letter of the correct definition next to the vocabulary word.

| | |
|---|---|
| ___ 11. imprecations | a. deceitfulness |
| ___ 12. ablution | b. kind |
| ___ 13. capricious | c. protest |
| ___ 14. unremunerative | d. curses |
| ___ 15. benevolent | e. flighty; unpredictable |
| ___ 16. avaricious | f. not profitable |
| ___ 17. dolefully | g. sorrowfully |
| ___ 18. duplicity | h. washing of the hands, body, etc. |
| ___ 19. placable | i. greedy |
| ___ 20. remonstrance | j. forgiving; capable of being appeased |

Name______________________________



**Write your answers on separate paper.**

**Short Answer:** Complete each sentence.

1. Pip helped the escaped convict because...
2. Pip was raised by his older sister, who mistreated him by...
3. One of the ways Joe showed kindness to Pip was by...
4. When Pip first met Miss Havisham, he was astonished to see that...
5. Estella made quite a contrast with Biddy; Estella was ________________ and ______________ while Biddy was _____________ and __________________.
6. Pip's sister became an invalid after...
7. Pip's expectations changed for the better when Mr. Jaggers brought the news that...
8. When Pip got to London, he discovered that his tutor's son was familiar to him because...
9. Pip began to understand Miss Havisham's attitude toward men when Herbert told him that 25 years earlier...
10. Mrs. Pocket's snobbery was evident from the way she complained continually about...

**Vocabulary:** Write a short definition for each word.

11. imprecations
12. ablution
13. capricious
14. unremunerative
15. benevolent
16. avaricious
17. dolefully
18. duplicity
19. placable
20. remonstrance

**Essay:** Answer both questions. (10 points each)

A. Meeting Estella has a profound impact on Pip. Describe how his attitude toward his home and his future changes after his first visit to Miss Havisham's.

B. Imagine that you are Pip. Explain what is going through his mind as he takes the carriage to London for the first time. Use your imagination as well as details from the story as you write down his thoughts.

Name______________________________



**Identification:** Find a character below who matches the description. Write the letter of the character next to the matching number. Each character is to be used only once.

| | | |
|---|---|---|
| A. Pip | B. Joe Gargery | C. Mrs. Joe Gargery |
| D. Mr. Pumblechook | E. Miss Havisham | F. Estella |
| G. Herbert Pocket | H. Mr. Jaggers | I. Wemmick |
| J. Bentley Drummle | K. Orlick | L. Abel Magwitch |

___ 1. This pompous corn-chandler took the credit for Pip's rise in expectations.
___ 2. The narrator of the story, he was orphaned before he ever knew his father or mother.
___ 3. This law clerk was dry and efficient at work, but loosened up at home with his father.
___ 4. A likable fellow, he became Pip's best friend.
___ 5. He attacked Pip's sister and later almost killed Pip.
___ 6. Pip's and Miss Havisham's bully of a lawyer, he held the power of life and death in many cases.
___ 7. He was the kind blacksmith who married Pip's sister and later Biddy.
___ 8. He was the convict who Pip helped on the marsh and who became Pip's anonymous benefactor.
___ 9. Pip's sister, she never tired of telling Pip what a trial it was to raise him.
___ 10. She cut herself off from the light of day after she was jilted on the day of her wedding.
___ 11. This brutal man married Estella.
___ 12. She was raised by Miss Havisham to break men's hearts.

**True/False:** Write "T" if the statement is true. Write "F" if it is false.
___ 13. When Joe came to visit Pip in London, Pip showed him the sights and took him to dinner.
___ 14. Pip assumed that Miss Havisham was grooming him to be married to Estella.
___ 15. Orlick hated Pip because Orlick wanted Estella for himself.
___ 16. Estella married Bentley Drummle even though she was not in love with him.
___ 17. Pip paid to get Herbert a job without Herbert's knowledge.
___ 18. Pip learned that the convict was his benefactor when Wemmick told him.
___ 19. The convict knew that he was breaking the law and risking death by returning to London to see Pip.

Name______________________________



___ 20. The convict hated Compeyson because he thought that Compeyson had done away with the convict's young daughter.
___ 21. Pip discovered that Wemmick's fiancee was Estella's mother.
___ 22. Estella started the fire that badly injured Miss Havisham.
___ 23. Miss Havisham asked Pip's forgiveness before she died.
___ 24. The convict finally gave himself up and was executed.
___ 25. Estella's husband was put in prison for beating his wife and died there.

**Sequencing:** Put the events in each set in chronological order by numbering them 1-5

<u>Set #1</u>
___ 26. Estella laughed when she saw Pip cry.
___ 27. Pip learned that he had an anonymous benefactor.
___ 28. Pip gave the convict food and a file.
___ 29. Pip was apprenticed to Joe Gargery as a blacksmith.
___ 30. Miss Havisham first invited Pip to come and play.

<u>Set #2</u>
___ 31. Pip learned that Miss Havisham was not his benefactress.
___ 32. The convict was recaptured and died soon after.
___ 33. Estella married Bentley Drummle.
___ 34. Miss Havisham was burned in a fire.
___ 35. Biddy married Joe.

**Analysis**: Select A or B and write a paragraph with complete sentences and at least three clearly explained examples. Indicate the letter of the question you answer.

A. Explain how Pip changes during the course of the novel.
B. Describe what Pip learns about the link between Miss Havisham, Estella, and the convict.

**Critical/Creative Thinking**: Select C or D. Remember to indicate the letter of your choice.

C. Support or contradict the following statement, using evidence from the story: *Pip helped Miss Havisham become a better person near the end of her life.*
D. Imagine you are Pip, five years after the end of the story. Write a letter to Joe and Biddy telling them about your life now.

Name______________________________



**Identification:** Choose the character that matches each quote. Write the letter of the character next to the matching number. Each character is to be used only once.

| | | | |
|---|---|---|---|
| A. Pip | B. Joe Gargery | C. Mrs. Joe | D. Mr. Pumblechook |
| E. Miss Havisham | F. Estella | G. Herbert Pocket | H. Mr. Jaggers |
| I. Wemmick | J. Bentley Drummle | K. Orlick | L. Abel Magwitch |

___ 1. "Be grateful, boy, to them which brought you up by hand."

___ 2. "I give Pirrip as my father's family name, on the authority of his tombstone..."

___ 3. "Every man's business is portable property."

___ 4. "Now Handel...will you come to me? Clara and I have talked about it again and again..."

___ 5. "It was you as did for your shrew sister...I give it her...I left her for dead..."

___ 6. "...Now I tell you what!...if you come here, bothering about your Bill, I'll make an example of both your Bill and you, and let him slip through my fingers. Have you paid Wemmick?"

___ 7. "Lookee here, old chap...Ever the best of friends; ain't us, Pip?"

___ 8. "Yes, Pip, dear boy, I've made a gentleman on you! It's me wot has done it!"

___ 9. "...giving holidays to great idle hulkers like that...I wish I was his master. I'd be a match for all noodles and rogues!"

___ 10. "Did I never give her a burning love, inseparable from jealousy at all times,...while she speaks thus to me! Let her call me mad!"

___ 11. (to Pip) "But don't lose your temper. Haven't you lost enough without that?"

___ 12. "Who taught me to be proud? Who praised me when I had learned my lesson?"

**Multiple Choice:** Circle the letter of the best answer.

13. Which does NOT describe Pip as a young man?
    (a) status-conscious
    (b) self-centered
    (c) thrifty
    (d) jealous

14. Which does NOT describe Miss Havisham when Pip first meets her?
    (a) mentally unbalanced
    (b) man-hater
    (c) controlling
    (d) pathological liar

15. If Herbert had not happened to find the dirty note telling Pip to go to the sluicehouse,
    (a) Orlick would have killed Pip
    (b) the convict would have escaped from England
    (c) Estella wouldn't have married Drummle
    (d) Herbert would not have left the country

16. If Compeyson hadn't alerted the authorities,
    (a) Orlick would have killed Pip
    (b) the convict would have escaped from England
    (c) Estella wouldn't have married Drummle
    (d) Herbert would not have left the country

17. The fact that Wemmick referred to the convict as "Tom, Jack, or Richard" indicated that Wemmick
    (a) disliked the convict and was unwilling to take the effort to recall his name
    (b) didn't want to admit his knowledge of the criminal by using the convict's real name
    (c) knew that Abel Magwitch used at least three aliases
    (d) had a poor memory for names and was becoming more and more like his Aged Parent

18. If Pip had been 21 in the U.S. today, he would probably choose to spend his Saturday on which activity?
    (a) a group hike along the Appalachian trail
    (b) drinks and gambling at Atlantic City
    (c) volunteering at a soup kitchen in the city
    (d) a game of horseshoes at a county fair

19. Like Orlick, Bentley Drummle
    (a) was a brutal man
    (b) was in love with Biddy
    (c) hated Pip for getting him fired
    (d) was from a wealthy family

20. Like Pip, Biddy
    (a) was Mrs. Gargery's sibling
    (b) had an anonymous benefactor
    (c) aspired to be a teacher
    (d) was an orphan

21. Which of the following is NOT a major theme in the story?
    (a) patriotic duty to one's country
    (b) inequities in the criminal justice system
    (c) relationships between men and women
    (d) maturation and self-discovery

22. Which of the following best describes Pip's attitude toward Biddy and Joe after he has spent a few months in London?
    (a) Pip grows angry with himself for having shared so many confidences with Biddy and Joe and worries that they might unwittingly endanger his prospects.
    (b) Pip grows increasingly angry with Biddy and Joe for their persistent efforts to keep in touch with him while he is trying to escape from their world.
    (c) Pip is often struck by the contrast between the dignity of his old friends and the shallowness of his new ones.
    (d) Pip spends little time thinking about his old friends, and when he does—he is embarrassed by their lack of refinement.

**True-False:** Write "T" if the statement is true. Write "F" if it is false. Use the back of your paper to rewrite false statements to make them true.

___ 23. Miss Havisham is aware that Pip believes she is his benefactor, and she allows him to think so.

___ 24. As an adult, Pip is repulsed by the convict at first but feels sympathy for him before the convict dies.

___ 25. *Great Expectations* is a bitter, humorless novel.

___ 26. Joe Gargery is a major vehicle of Dickens' moral insight.

___ 27. Joe Gargery is a figure of good-humored fun.

___ 28. As Pip's position unravels, so does his moral stature.

___ 29. As Pip, Magwitch, Herbert, and Startop row toward the steamship, all that Pip can think about is himself.

___ 30. Miss Havisham had brought Estella up without love, and accepted that Estella could not love even her.

___ 31. Miss Havisham begged Pip to forgive her at the end, but he could not bring himself to do so.

___ 32. At the end of the novel, Pip finally accepted that he and Estella could never be together.

**Short Essay:** Answer each question in one or two sentences. (Use the back of your paper.)

33. Why did Orlick hate Pip so much?

34. Why did Pip ask Miss Havisham for money?

35. Why did Miss Havisham alter her will?

36. What was "fitting" about the way that Estella's husband died?

37. Why did Pip leave the country for eleven years?

## Written Response

**Analysis:** Select A or B and indicate the letter of the question you decide to answer. Choose the alternative that best represents your opinion, and explain the reasons for your choice in a short paragraph. Cite evidence from the book to support your opinion. Write your paragraph on a separate sheet of paper.

A. By continuing to love Estella through all the years when she rejected him, Pip reveals his
   (1) inability to see her as she is
   (2) inability to control his own hopeless infatuation
   (3) faith that Estella is capable of change
   (4) other

B. If Pip were alive today, his personality traits would best qualify him to be a(n)
   (1) actor
   (2) politician who promotes prison reform
   (3) advocate for abused children
   (4) other

**Critical and Creative Writing:** Select C or D.

C. Explain why you do or do not feel that the conclusion to *Great Expectations* is a satisfying one. Include a discussion of the alternative ending that Dickens first considered—and why you do or do not prefer that one.

D. You write the "Dear Gabby" column in a nationally-circulated newspaper. Write the letter that you receive from Pip about his problematic infatuation. Then write your answer.

# Answer Key

**Activity #1:** Students should be encouraged to discuss their answers to this and other open-ended activities, for which there are no "right" or "wrong" answers.

**STUDY QUESTIONS**

**Chapters 1-7:** 1-in the cemetery; Pip is visiting the graves of his parents and brothers. 2-get him a file and some food; Pip is afraid that the convict will send the ferocious "young man" after him otherwise. 3-the cane Pip's sister uses to beat him; His sister threw him at her husband. 4-a terrible-tasting home remedy; After pouring out some brandy for the convict, Pip accidentally tops off the brandy bottle with the Tar-water. 5-another escaped convict; surprised, angry, eager to "pull down" the other convict; 6-Mr. Wopsle, Mr. and Mrs. Hubble, Uncle Pumblechook; they reproach him, tell him to be grateful. 7-It is his way of comforting Pip. 8-They need him to fix some handcuffs. 9-The original convict is fighting with him. 10-He tells everyone that he stole the food and drink—probably to keep Pip from being blamed. 11-He can't bring himself to tell Joe about the theft any more than he could keep himself from stealing the food and file in the first place. 12-He learns very little from his teacher; he teaches himself with Biddy's help. 13-Wealthy Miss Havisham has spoken to Pumblechook about finding a boy to entertain her.

**Chapters 8-12:** 1-The seeds stuck to everyone's pants. 2-Pip's breakfast is meager while Mr. Pumblechook's is lavish. 3-She is scornful; calls him "boy." 4-Dressed in a wedding gown, sitting in the dark, she is ghastly and death-like, like a wax figure. 5-by playing cards; 6-Estella has insulted him repeatedly, called him a clumsy laboring boy, and he feels humiliated and angry. 7-Miss Havisham hanging by the neck from a beam; 8-He dreads being misunderstood, so makes up a fabulous tale. 9-As Pip's sister shoved his face against the kitchen wall, Pip became more determined to keep the truth from her. 10-The stranger stirs his drink with a file; he gives Pip a shilling wrapped in two one-pound notes. 11-several of her relatives; She doesn't seem to like the Pockets and thinks they are after her money. 12-after he fights with the pale boy; The boy was friendly and not an efficient fighter. Estella acted as if the kiss were worth nothing. 13-Biddy; 14-Joe; Pip's sister has not been invited.

**Chapters 13-18:** 1-to ask about Pip's apprenticeship; Joe talks to Pip instead of to Miss Havisham. 2-25 guineas as a "premium" for the time Pip has spent with her; She wants to make sure they expect no more money from her. 3-He appeases his wife by inventing the idea that Miss Havisham sent her respects. 4-An apprentice is legally bound to his master to work for a certain period; Mr. Pumblechook. 5-He is ashamed of his home and dislikes blacksmithing because Estella has made him feel coarse. 6-He is so miserable that he might run away, if it weren't for Joe's trust in him. 7-Biddy; Mr. Wopsle only wants him as a dramatic lay-figure for his own acting. 8-Joe goes off on a tangent about why these would be unsuitable gifts for her. 9-a menacing man who works for Joe; Orlick's slouch makes Pip think of the way Cain might have walked around after killing his brother. 10-Orlick has insulted Joe's wife, who criticized Joe for giving Orlick time off. 11-She is abroad, learning to be "a lady." 12-Someone attacks her and hits her on the head; Pip suspects Orlick or the stranger who gave him the money. 13-She died; Biddy comes to live with Pip's family. 14-She seems to want to be on good terms with him. 15-that he will inherit a handsome property from an anonymous benefactor who wants him to start being brought up as a gentleman

**Chapters 19-23:** 1-She balks when he suggests that she help Joe with his learning and manners, saying that Joe is proud. 2-He is warm and effusive now that Pip has money. 3-He probably resents Mr. Trabb's ordering him about as if he is not Pip's equal. 4-He assumes that she is the one who is giving him his fortune. 5-He bullies them, then asks repeatedly if they have paid. 6-the son of Pip's tutor; He is the pale young gentleman Pip had fought with at Miss Havisham's, years before. 7-"Handel"—after a composer who wrote a piece of music about a blacksmith; 8-She was jilted by her fiancé after he and her half-brother extracted money from her; she raised Estella to wreak revenge on men. 9-She didn't marry someone of noble birth; her grandfather's father should have been made a baronet. 10-at least seven; It is a chaotic family and neither children nor parents are particularly happy.

**Chapters 24-30:** 1-He wants money for furniture so that he can stay at the inn instead of moving in with the Pockets; he gets it, but Jaggers is disagreeable about it. 2-He is eating crackers as if he were posting letters into his mouth. 3-It was given to him by a convict awaiting execution; Wemmick makes sure that he gets all that he can from executed prisoners. 4-Bentley Drummle; 5-relatives of Miss Havisham's who assume that she is giving him money that is rightfully theirs; 6-He is so sure of his powers of intimidation that he leaves his doors open to show that he knows no one would dare rob him. 7-His office is dusty, cluttered, dreary; his home has been carefully fixed up as a cozy replica of a castle. 8-Wemmick's old father; Wemmick dotes on his father. 9-Pip, Herbert, Drummle, and Startop; He is interested in Drummle. 10-She pants, seems anxious, has strong, scarred wrists. 11-Drummle had almost attacked Startop. 12-to let him know that Joe is coming for a visit; She doesn't want to injure Joe's pride by letting him see the line where she expresses her hope that he will still want to see his old friend "even though a gentleman." 13-Joe has informed him that Estella is home and ready to see him. 14-Pip's servant; 15-One is the man who gave Pip the shilling wrapped in the one-pound notes. 16-Pip has just told the waiter not to send for Pumblechook; the waiter probably wants Pip to see the article in which Pumblechook takes credit as the founder of Pip's fortunes. 17-She is more womanly, but still treats him as a boy. 18-He assumes that Miss Havisham is raising him to be a gentleman so that he can marry Estella; Miss Havisham tells him to "love her." 19-Pip tells Jaggers (Miss Havisham's attorney) that Orlick is not trustworthy enough to be working for Miss Havisham; Pip has always mistrusted Orlick—especially since the attack on his sister and since Biddy's revelation that he "dances at" her. 20-Still smarting from the put-downs he received from Trabb while outfitting Pip, Trabb's boy makes fun of Pip and his gentlemanly appearance.

**Chapters 31-37**: 1-Hamlet; references to Ophelia and Denmark; the acting is laughable. 2-to visit with the prisoners, obtain "portable property" from those facing execution; 3-She sends a note telling him to meet her; she is on her way to Richmond to stay with a woman who will introduce her to society. 4-ironic; Pip and Herbert spent a lot of money irresponsibly on expensive food, drink, etc. 5-Joe's wife has died and it would be improper for Biddy to stay on; she is looking for a teaching job. 6-500 pounds; 7-Mr. Wemmick's prim-and-proper lady friend; 8-In his official capacity, he is against lending money because it is fiscally irresponsible; at home, where he can speak freely, he would support helping out a friend. 9-Miss Skiffins' brother conducts a negotiation whereby some of Pip's money is used to pay a merchant to hire Herbert. 10-Unreceptive—she removes his arm from her waist.

**Chapters 38-43**: 1-She uses him to tease her other admirers. 2-Estella draws her hand away from Miss Havisham's. 3-At the Finches club, he proposes a toast to her. 4-The convict shows up at his door in the rain and tells all; Jaggers; 5-New South Wales (Australia; prisoners formerly kept in hulks moored in the Thames were sent to Botany Bay); 6-The convict is forbidden to return to England and faces execution. 7-Abel Magwitch; Provis; 8-Herbert helps him plan to get the convict onto a boat for Hamburg or somewhere else. 9-Compeyson was a gentlemanly criminal whom the convict worked for. When Compeyson—the suitor who jilted Miss Havisham—and the convict were both caught, Compeyson made sure that he was let off more easily than Magwitch, so Magwitch attacked him on the prison ship and both escaped (the day Pip first met Magwitch). 10-He meets Drummle on the way to Estella's.

**Chapters 44-50**: 1-Who am I to be kind? 2-Bentley Drummle; she says that he won't notice as other men might that she doesn't love him. 3-Wemmick; he knows that Pip's rooms are being watched by someone who wishes Magwitch ill. 4-Magwitch; in a house by the river where Herbert's fiancée and her father live; 5-Herbert's fiancée; She waits hand and foot on her alcoholic father. 6-He sees Compeyson—the "other convict" he had seen years before—standing behind Pip. 7-constantly washes his hands; 8-He notices the resemblance between the servant and Estella. 9-Wemmick tells Pip about how Jaggers "tamed" the murderess who had killed another woman and supposedly killed her child. 10-Pip gets her to agree to send money for Herbert's benefit. 11-She reveals that she asked Jaggers to bring her a girl to love; under her name, the words "I forgive her" 12-He senses something wrong and finds her in flames. 13-Herbert repeats what Provis has been telling him.

**Chapters 51-56**: 1-Provis/Magwitch; Pip tells Jaggers, because he wants Jaggers in return to tell him all he knows about Estella. 2-Jaggers defended her mother in a murder case and brought her to Miss Havisham to be raised. 3-Pip agrees that it would cast Estella into disgrace and do no good. 4-He

insists on crying and talking about his feelings after his daughter is arrested. 5-Cairo; Pip has been sending money to the merchant who has hired Herbert. 6-Startop is the young boarder Pip met when he first went to Herbert's; Herbert asks Startop to do some rowing without explaining that he will be rowing a convict to safety. 7-He receives a letter and assumes it has something to do with the plans for getting the convict out of the country; Orlick tries to kill him. 8-Herbert shows up at the sluice house with Trabb's boy and Startop. 9-There is no time, if they are to go through with their plan for getting the convict out of the country. 10-Compeyson alerts the authorities, who arrive in a small boat just as the convict and Pip are about to board the steamer. 11-Compeyson and his spies have been watching Pip and sending false information about Compeyson's whereabouts. 12-The convict knocks him overboard, they grapple, and Compeyson drowns. 13-to see him get married; 14-He is sentenced to be executed. 15-The convict's daughter is alive, a beautiful lady, and Pip loves her.
**Chapters 57-59 + Appendices:** 1-His bills pile up and he gets sick. 2-Joe tells him that Miss Havisham left a lot of money to Matthew, Herbert's father, because of Pip's putting in a good word for him. 3-He is arrested after breaking into Pumblechook's house. 4-Joe has paid off the debt. 5-He plans to ask her hand in marriage but finds that she has married Joe. 6-He joins Herbert in business and leaves England for Cairo. 7-Her husband has treated her brutally; they separated; he was killed in an accident caused by his mistreating a horse. 8-After a visit to Joe's family, Pip goes to say good-bye to Satis and finds Estella outside, doing the same. 9-Her touch is now friendly; she realizes what she threw away by rejecting him; "I saw no shadow of another parting from her."

**Activity #2:** 1-A; 2-B; 3-A; 4-D; 5-D; 6-A; 7-D; 8-C; 9-B; 10-B; 11-D; 12-A; 13-B; 14-B; 15-D
**Activity #3:** 1-gourmandising—gluttonous; eating excessively: 2-transfixed—frozen in place and time; stopped: 3-capricious—impulsive, mercurial; 4-ignominiously—humiliatingly; 5-adamantine—unyieldingly hard in attitude; 6-felicitous—fitting, suitable; 7-appalled—dismayed, horrified; 8-sanguinary—bloody; 9-trepidation—anxiety, terror; 10-unremunerative—not profitable
A-4; B-2; C-7; D-8; E-1; F-10; G-9; H-6; I-3; J-5
**Activity #4:** 1-A; 2-E; 3-B; 4-A; 5-C; 6-E; 7-D; 8-B; 9-A; 10-B
**Activity #5:** 1-E; 2-A; 3-C; 4-B; 5-A; 6-E; 7-A; 8-C; 9-B; 10-A; 11-C; 12-D; 13-D; 14-B; 15-A
**Activity #6:** 1-E; 2-D; 3-B; 4-E; 5-A; 6-D; 7-C
**Activity #7:** 1-Both have to do with oral speech. 2-Both are positive attitudes toward someone. 3-Both are restraints put on prisoners. 4-Both are tanks for holding water. 5-Both refer to a secondary, lesser person. 6-Both are part of the criminal justice system. 7-Both ask for a favor. 8-Both go on the feet. 9-Both work with horses. 10-Both are skirts. 11-Both are connected with death. 12-Both are places where people work by cutting into the earth. 13-Both involve trips. 14-Both are flags. 15-Both go around the waist.
**Activity #8:** Predictions will vary. 1-wan—pale; 2-sconces—brackets for candles placed on a wall; 3-ingrate—ungrateful person; 4-beseeching—begging, pleading; 5-untenable—cannot be held or defended, as an idea; 6-dram—small drink of liquor; 7-prolix—long and wordy; 8-dubiously—doubtfully; 9-uncouth—boorish, discourteous; 10-physiognomy—face; 11-expatriated—exiled; 12-pannikins—small metal cups or pans; 13-pretext—alibi, excuse; 14-transport—convict sent into banishment; 15-vagrancy—wandering without permanent address or employment; 16-extenuated—served to make a fault less serious; 17-insolent—bold, brash; 18-superciliously—arrogantly
**Activity #9:** 1-braided; 2-very old; 3-fierce; 4-magic; 5-quivering, trembling; 6-decayed, withered; 7-acquit, exonerate; 8-begged, pleaded; 9-sympathy; 10-foreboding; feeling of something about to happen; 11-remainder; 12-5; 13-7; 14-3; 15-8; 16-1; 17-9; 18-11
**Activity #10:** 1-I; 2-G; 3-A; 4-T; 5-N; 6-Q; 7-J; 8-R; 9-H; 10-D; 11-B; 12-E; 13-C; 14-F; 15-M; 16-K; 17-L; 18-P; 19-O; 20-S
**Activity #11:** Set 1-orthographical; Set 2-debilitating; Set 3-ostentatious; Set 4-vestige

**Activity #12:** Sociograms will vary but should reflect that Pip is infatuated with Estella, while he has little emotional impact on her; Pip loves Joe but soon rejects him out of embarrassment while Joe remains faithful to Pip; Pip is somewhat frightened by strange Miss Havisham, but does her bidding while she considers him a plaything, and, as a member of the male sex—someone who deserves to be hurt; the convict frightens Pip into helping him and seems somewhat grateful, while Pip is terrified of the convict.
**Activity #13:** Answers will vary; Venn diagrams should reflect that both women raise children who aren't their own, in a harsh environment; Miss Havisham has no husband and hates men while Mrs. Gargery has a doting husband whom she abuses.
**Activity #14:** Answers will vary. These coincidences might be mentioned: the convict turns out to be Estella's father; the convict's enemy turns out to be the man who jilted Miss Havisham; Miss Havisham's half-brother Arthur dies near 5 o'clock—just when he said he would; the convict who gave Pip the money ends up seated behind him years later.
**Activity #15:** Answers will vary. Most will agree that Mrs. Joe, Jaggers, Pumblechook, Compeyson, Drummle, and Orlick belong in several negative categories.
**Activity #16:** Answers will vary. Students should be encouraged to summarize aloud and discuss what is shown on the finished chart.
**Activity #17:** Answers will vary. Most will agree that Pip is a good-hearted, social-climbing, fun-loving people watcher while both Bentley Drummle and Estella are aloof, wealthy, and self-centered.
**Activity #18:** Answers will vary.
**Activity #19:** Students should be encouraged to help each other revise ongoing drafts and to share the finished products.

**Comprehension Quiz, Level I**
1-F; because he was afraid the convict would send someone after him if he didn't bring back food and a file; 2-T; 3-T; 4-T; 5-F; Biddy was plain and kind while Estella was beautiful and cold; 6-T; 7-F; that an anonymous donor would pay to make him a gentleman; 8-F; they had fought; 9-T; 10-T; 11-D; 12-H; 13-E; 14-F; 15-B; 16-I; 17-G; 18-A; 19-J; 20-C
**Comprehension Quiz, Level II**
1-he was afraid that if he didn't, the convict would send someone after him. 2-beating him and criticizing him constantly. 3-trying to help him avoid beatings. 4-she wore an old wedding dress and had an ancient wedding cake kept on a table. 5-beautiful and cold while Biddy was plain and kind. 6-an attacker hit her over the head. 7-an anonymous donor was paying for him to become a gentleman. 8-they had fought as boys at Miss Havisham's. 9-she had been jilted on her wedding day by her fiancé. 10-not having married someone of noble birth. 11-curses; 12-washing; 13-impulsive and mercurial; 14-unprofitable; 15-kind and generous; 16-greedy; 17-sadly; 18-deceitfulness; 19-capable of being appeased; forgiving; 20-protest. Essay: A-The essay should describe how Pip begins to despise his home and his "lowly" background, and is no longer content to become a blacksmith. B-The answer might contain a mixture of hopeful feelings and anxious thoughts.

**Novel Test, Level I**
Identification: 1-D; 2-A; 3-I; 4-G; 5-K; 6-H; 7-B; 8-L; 9-C; 10-E; 11-J; 12-F
True/False: 13-F; 14-T; 15-F; 16-T; 17-T; 18-F; 19-T; 20-F; 21-F; 22-F; 23-T; 24-F; 25-F
Sequencing: 26-3; 27-5; 28-1; 29-4; 30-2; 31-1; 32-4; 33-2; 34-3; 35-5
Analysis: A. The answer should refer to the fact that Pip acquires social graces and vices, and eventually becomes more mature and humble.
B. The convict is Estella's father; Miss Havisham had been jilted by the man who later hired the convict and ultimately caused his recapture by the authorities.
Critical/Creative Thinking: C. Most answers will support the statement by describing how Pip's loyalty to Miss Havisham and his willingness to forgive her enable her finally to express affection to him ("Dear boy") and to realize how she has wronged both Pip and Estella.

D. Answers will vary, but most will probably assume that Pip is happily married to Estella, working hard and making an adequate income.

**Novel Test, Level II**

Identification: 1-D; 2-A; 3-I; 4-G; 5-K; 6-H; 7-B; 8-L; 9-C; 10-E; 11-J; 12-F
Multiple Choice: 13-C; 14-D; 15-A; 16-B; 17-B; 18-B; 19-A; 20-D; 21-A; 22-D
True-False: 23-T; 24-T; 25-F; There is a great deal of wry humor in this novel. 26-T; 27-T; 28-F; As Pip's position unravels, his moral stature rises and he becomes a "better person." 29-F; Pip concentrates on the convict. 30-F; Miss Havisham loved Estella in a twisted way, and grew angry when she found that Estella did not return affection to her. 31-F; and he did forgive her. 32-F; Pip and Estella did get together.
Short Essay: 33-When Pip was young, he felt that Pip would take over his job in the blacksmith shop; later Pip caused him to lose his job with Miss Havisham. 34-Pip felt that he couldn't take any more money from the convict; he wanted to help Herbert get a position. 35-Pip convinced her that her relative, Matthew, was deserving. 36-A brutal man, he died in an accident caused by his abuse of a horse. 37-He went abroad to work with Herbert.
Written Response: A. Students who choose (1) may defend the idea that Pip could not accept the fact that Estella was incapable of loving anyone. Those who choose (2) may defend the proposition that Pip knew how hopeless his situation was; he did get angry with Estella for humiliating him and realized that she was being unkind, but he could not think of life without her—to the point where he didn't even marry when she had married someone else. Those who choose (3) may point out that he had seen how the convict had changed at the end of his life; perhaps Pip felt that he could show Estella how to express love.

B. Students who choose (1) may point out that Pip enjoyed going to plays and, as this story attests, is adept at watching people and reading their expressions. Perhaps he would enjoy focusing that ability into an acting career. Students who choose (2) may point to his criticisms of the prison system throughout the novel—from his description of the Hulks to his observations on Newgate. Those who choose (3) may feel that Pip—a physically abused child who grew up and married someone who had been emotionally abused—would be interested in protecting other children from abuse.

Answers for C and D will vary.